Dalesman Books — 1991

The Dalesman Publishing Company Ltd.
Clapham, via Lancaster, LA2 8EB.

First published 1991
© Barry Knowles 1991

ISBN: 1 85568 032 7

For Gill

Printed by J.W. Lambert & Sons, Station Road, Settle, North Yorkshire.

SHEEP DROPPINGS

SCENE: The Dalesman offices

"Did you know that 'The Black Sheep' was a tribe which established a principality in Armenia that lasted 108 years, from 1360-1468...?"

"Why am I being given this ridiculous information?"

"And that 'The White Sheep' was a tribe which established another Armenian rabble from 1468 all the way through till 1508 when, apparently they started wearing Acrilan?"

"Have you been at the Sheep Dip again..."

"No I just found my library ticket and have been grazing through 'Brewer's Phrase and Fable'..."

"In other words you've done another sheep book...?"

"Yes. What do you think of it...?"

"Well, it's just another load of Sheep Droppings..."

"Glad you approve. Shall we adjourn to the ale house...?"

MORE SHEEP DROPPINGS

*"I'd rather **not** be 'best turned out' at the sheep fair
than put up with all this faffing about..."*

MORE SHEEP DROPPINGS

*"You want to get yourself clipped—there's a couple
of cuckoo's eggs in there..."*

MORE SHEEP DROPPINGS

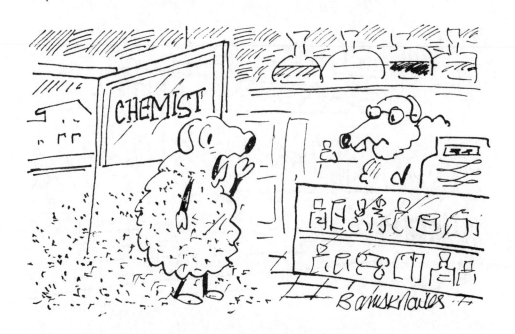

"Quick! A bottle of Vosene anti-dandruff sheep dip..."

MORE SHEEP DROPPINGS

MORE SHEEP DROPPINGS

MORE SHEEP DROPPINGS

MORE SHEEP DROPPINGS

MORE SHEEP DROPPINGS

*"Have a good day at school and don't accept bunches of
grass from strangers . . ."*

*"Could you drag our shepherd from under the table
and tell him his barn's burning down..."*

MORE SHEEP DROPPINGS

"There's no way I'm going to walk over and take myself to the French market..."

MORE SHEEP DROPPINGS

MORE SHEEP DROPPINGS

*"Dad—I've got six hundred and seven young ewes
into trouble..."*

MORE SHEEP DROPPINGS

*"Nothing much this week—a couple of bit parts in
The Archers and a crowd scene for Emmerdale . . ."*

*"Why didn't you tell me there was an archery range
in the next field...?"*

"Looks like they're going to build some new council houses..."

MORE SHEEP DROPPINGS

"I knew it was a mistake buying then a trampoline..."

"I made it out of a clapped out satellite dish..."

MORE SHEEP DROPPINGS

"That's the third year running I've fallen asleep during haymaking..."

MORE SHEEP DROPPINGS

"I haven't slept a wink since those Welsh sheep moved in next door..."

MORE SHEEP DROPPINGS

MORE SHEEP DROPPINGS

MORE SHEEP DROPPINGS

MORE SHEEP DROPPINGS

"Pardon me madam, but have I tupped you yet..."

*"You're suffering from what we call **'shear** desperation'..."*

MORE SHEEP DROPPINGS

MORE SHEEP DROPPINGS

"I always thought Wordsworth was a bit of a weirdo..."

MORE SHEEP DROPPINGS

"Don't tell me—he's conducting the BAAccarolle..."

MORE SHEEP DROPPINGS

MORE SHEEP DROPPINGS

"We'er your new neighbours from Sellafield..."

MORE SHEEP DROPPINGS

"Which of the trippers are likely to have left decent picnic remains..."

MORE SHEEP DROPPINGS

"That's all we need—low-flying seagulls..."

"*Other countries have the greenhouse effect—we have the Frigidaire effect...*"

MORE SHEEP DROPPINGS

"I'm sick to death of darning you two..."

*"I'd like to change that to 'forsaking **no** others'..."*

MORE SHEEP DROPPINGS

*"Two double **Baa**cardis..."*

"I can offer you a garden flat or the top of the hill penthouse..."

MORE SHEEP DROPPINGS

"Things are going so badly—my husband and I are sleeping on separate fells..."

MORE SHEEP DROPPINGS

MORE SHEEP DROPPINGS

"Their father was a ram who fell off the back of a knacker's yard lorry..."

MORE SHEEP DROPPINGS

"The poor little lad lost his puppy and I'm the alternative..."

"Wow! I'm down to one bag full..."

"A double bracken-burger and a nettle shake..."

MORE SHEEP DROPPINGS

"Don't look now, but it's David Attenborbour ough..."

MORE SHEEP DROPPINGS

MORE SHEEP DROPPINGS

*"Don't erect your gamp—it **is** acid rain..."*

MORE SHEEP DROPPINGS

"Have you a three minute ring..."

MORE SHEEP DROPPINGS

"One hundred and seventeen pregnancy testing kits, please..."

MORE SHEEP DROPPINGS

*"According to this pillock of a lexicographer we're
'Any of a genus of ruminant mammals having tansversely
ribbed horns and a narrow face...'"*

MORE SHEEP DROPPINGS

"So much for the silly superstition—He's just eaten a four-leafed clover..."

MORE SHEEP DROPPINGS

"Well, this should screw up the Glasgow-Euston Express..."

MORE SHEEP DROPPINGS

"I daren't come out—I've lost my trunks..."

MORE SHEEP DROPPINGS

MORE SHEEP DROPPINGS

"A packet of 750 for the weekend please . . . "

MORE SHEEP DROPPINGS

*"I could make out a very good case for **ewe**-thenasia..."*

MORE SHEEP DROPPINGS

MORE SHEEP DROPPINGS

"I think that insurance salesman has just fleeced us..."

MORE SHEEP DROPPINGS

"I've met a dishy young tup—should I go on the pill...?"

MORE SHEEP DROPPINGS

"The sheepdog's taught him to cock his leg..."

MORE SHEEP DROPPINGS

"We'er so lucky to be away from all life's crass
commercialism, living in unspoilt beauty..."

MORE SHEEP DROPPINGS

"Who's the white trash..."

MORE SHEEP DROPPINGS

"I see homo sapiens has a tupping season too..."

MORE SHEEP DROPPINGS

*"If you want to cut out the middleman, we can let you
have the stuff wholesale..."*

*"Somehow I don't think Bo Peep will **ever** find her sheep..."*

MORE SHEEP DROPPINGS

"I prefer to take my own bathroom preparations..."

MORE SHEEP DROPPINGS

"Bad news, girls—he's got rid of the collie and bought a pit bull terrier..."

MORE SHEEP DROPPINGS

"Hey Ma—I've brought a few kids home for tea..."

MORE SHEEP DROPPINGS

MORE SHEEP DROPPINGS

MORE SHEEP DROPPINGS

MORE SHEEP DROPPINGS

"I've divided the fell into plots that we can flog as timeshare units..."

MORE SHEEP DROPPINGS

"Look! A shepherd's crook..."

*"Have you met that nut? They call him **Ram**sky-Korsakov..."*

MORE SHEEP DROPPINGS

"I think I know what they mean by a shepherd spy..."

MORE SHEEP DROPPINGS

"I refuse to go to any sheep fair while it's persisting down..."

MORE SHEEP DROPPINGS

MORE SHEEP DROPPINGS

MORE SHEEP DROPPINGS

"I warned you to pay your fell tax bill..."

MORE SHEEP DROPPINGS

"I never thought our wool would end up as sporrans..."

MORE SHEEP DROPPINGS

"I got caught by a runaway strimmer..."

"Don't you dare start gambolling..."

*"You have all the symptoms of acute cirrhosis of
your lamb's liver..."*

"How do you fancy a double-glazed, centrally heated sheep pen in Borrowdale..."

MORE SHEEP DROPPINGS

"Didn't we have a lovverly time the day we went to RAMSgate..."

"I've just made a nasty ewe-turn..."

MORE SHEEP DROPPINGS

"The pensions have gone up—we now get two hectares of grass a week..."